Other cartoon giftbooks in this series:
The Crazy World of Cats
The Crazy World of Football
The Crazy World of Gardening
The Crazy World of Golf
The Crazy World of Marriage
The Crazy World of Sex

This paperback edition published simultaneously in 1998 by Exley
Publications Ltd in Great Britain, and Exley Publications LLC in the USA.
First hardback edition published in 1997 by Exley Publications Ltd in Great
Britain, and Exley Publications LLC in the USA.

12 11 10 9 8 7 6 5 4 3 2 1

Copyright © Bill Stott, 1998

ISBN 1-86187-107-4

Printed in Malta.

Exley Publications Ltd, 16 Chalk Hill, Watford, Herts WD1 4BN, United
Kingdom.
Exley Publications LLC, 232 Madison Avenue, Suite 1206, NY 10016, USA.

THE Crazy WORLD OF BOWLS

CARTOONS BY
BILL STOTT

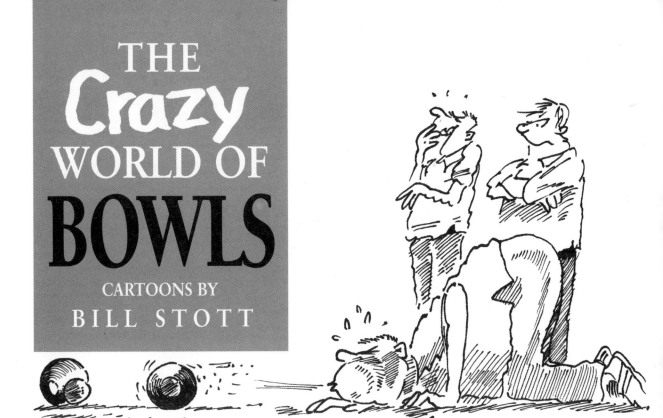

 **EXLEY**
NEW YORK • WATFORD, UK

"I'm getting just a bit fed up of you re-living the deciding end, Gordon...."

"I'm pleased he's got a hobby – I just wish he wouldn't use the adjoining wall!"

"'*Course I don't just live for bowls. There's er.... Then, there's... er... er....*"

"Look! A blue bit!"

"So, you're quite keen on bowls are you, Henry?"

"That's the Wilkinsons. Identical track suits, caps, bags – and oddly enough, they're just as bad as each other at bowls...."

"*So, we came to the final end, and talk about nip and tuck, I'll tell you, my heart was in my mouth. Then young Carl Phillips says to me, he says....*"

"Hello Mrs. Jones... 'is back's gone again...."

"Sorry about that... trying out a new overarm delivery... hand slipped...."

"For really important matches, I can never decide which set to use."

"His other hobby is bowls...."

"We were expecting a tough match, but this is ridiculous...."

"Whoops!"

"Frankly, I've played on better surfaces...."

"This is the cut-price set you were telling me about?"

"'Course as a new member you weren't to know that big Hilda always crushes a couple of bowls before a match. Unnerves the opposition, she reckons...."

"New to it is he? We don't often see a run-up...."

"Thank you!"

"I mean, it's like all you live for is bowls. Bowls, bowls, bowls – I just think we're missing so much – and will you stop polishing those things whilst I'm talking to you?"

"*Yes, yes... worms. We're bound to get the odd one. Calm down....*"

"Ignore it. They're just trying to psyche you out...."

"Wow! Here comes another crateful!"

NEANDERTHAL BOWLS

"O.K. It's good – but it's not bowls – and I had such hopes for the boy...."

"It's not me, is it?"

"I know, I know! My wife's better than me – and I hate it! D' you hear? I hate it!"

"Right – nearest the jack or you're sawdust, pal."

"But it's not my dog!"

"I don't like the look of this...."

"Don't be alarmed – it's traditional that the Fairfield match always starts with a brawl...."

"A bit keen, the opposition...."

"*He usually starts from here when he's having a practice. We've only got a short back garden....*"

"There's nothing wrong with saying 'hard luck' – but you'll <u>have</u> to learn not to snigger...."

"Superglue on the jack is just not funny any more, Ted...."

"I know we're not an ageist club. I know she's good, but she's playing havoc with the older members' nerves...."

"I'm all for bringing bowls to the country's youth, but is Gordon the right ambassador?"

"Leaves nothing to chance, your partner?"

"I'd just like to remind you that there is a time limit in league matches...."

"'Course since the game's made it big on T.V., Bernard's insisting on make-up before each end...."

"He's such a bighead – but don't worry – there isn't a cassette in it!"

"Nothing like a bit of friendly rivalry."

"Uh uh – Hell's bowlers!"

"There's nothing in the rules about it...."

"I think he's what they call 'an umpire's umpire'...."

"It's his own fault – the doctor's warned him about overuse of the forehand."

"Which reminds me, Jerry – how's the floodlights fund coming along?"

"*I'm all for it becoming more popular, but this is silly.*"

"Stop moaning and get on with it – a sponsor's a sponsor!"

"*I know they're two leagues below us, but try not to be so casual....*"

"Well... I've seen better...."

"... can't stand folk who show off when they're winning...."

"The old stand was never built to take a Mexican wave...."

"I know we want to make bowls a 'now' thing, but you do look a bit silly Gerald...."

"Why don't you buy a case for them like everyone else?"

"For Heaven's sake, Muriel – we need the jack!"

"Typical, isn't it – taught her all I know, now, she's ten times better than me!"

"Personally, I think it's a great shame the senior member of the team doesn't like the new strip!"

*"Will you stop panicking! Hardacre's not developed a new technique.
He's just had a hernia operation!"*

"Funny how she always manages to faint during her last end."

"I see Charlie Fairclough didn't win the championship again this year...."

"Proposing? Don't be silly – he's having a practice...."

"Why can't you be like normal lottery winners and buy flash cars and world cruises?"

"Yes, they __are__ just kids. Yes, they __are__ muscling in our game... and yes, they did beat us!"

"It's the local news channel wanting to know how you're coping with defeat after the Windyridge bowls final...."

"And to cousin Derek, I leave my unique collection of bowls...."

TOMB OF THE UNKNOWN BOWLER

"Hello Darling. Did you win?"

Books in "The World's Greatest" series

The World's Greatest Business Cartoons
The World's Greatest Cat Cartoons
The World's Greatest Computer Cartoons
The World's Greatest Dad Cartoons
The World's Greatest Do-It-Yourself Cartoons
The World's Greatest Golf Cartoons
The World's Greatest Keep Fit Cartoons
The World's Greatest Marriage Cartoons
The World's Greatest Middle Age Cartoons
The World's Greatest Rugby Cartoons
The World's Greatest Sex Cartoons

Books in the "Victim's Guide" series

Award-winning cartoonist Roland Fiddy sees the funny side to life's phobias, nightmares and catastrophes.

The Victim's Guide to Air Travel
The Victim's Guide to The Baby
The Victim's Guide to The Boss
The Victim's Guide to Christmas
The Victim's Guide to The Dentist
The Victim's Guide to The Doctor
The Victim's Guide to Middle Age

Books in the "Crazy World" series

The Crazy World of Aerobics
The Crazy World of Hospitals
The Crazy World of The Office
The Crazy World of Sailing
The Crazy World of School

The following titles in this series are available in paperback and also in a full colour mini hardback edition

The Crazy World of Bowls
The Crazy World of Cats
The Crazy World of Football
The Crazy World of Gardening
The Crazy World of Golf
The Crazy World of Housework
The Crazy World of Marriage
The Crazy World of Rugby
The Crazy World of Sex

Books in the "Fanatic's Guide" series

The **Fanatic's Guides** are perfect presents for everyone with a hobby that has got out of hand. Eighty pages of hilarious black and white cartoons by Roland Fiddy.

The Fanatic's Guide to Dogs
The Fanatic's Guide to Money
The Fanatic's Guide to Sports

The following titles in this series are available in paperback and also in a full colour mini hardback edition

The Fanatic's Guide to Cats
The Fanatic's Guide to Computers
The Fanatic's Guide to Dads
The Fanatic's Guide to D.I.Y.
The Fanatic's Guide to Golf
The Fanatic's Guide to Husbands
The Fanatic's Guide to Love
The Fanatic's Guide to Sex
The Wrinklies Guide to Staying Young at Heart
The Mobile Phone Cartoon Book